BRILL

THINGS TO
MAKE
AND DO

FOR 6 YEAR OLDS

Kingfisher Books, Grisewood & Dempsey Ltd, Elsley House,
24–30 Great Titchfield Street, London W1P 7AD

First published in 1994 by Kingfisher Books
10 9 8 7 6 5 4 3 2 1
© Grisewood & Dempsey Ltd 1994

BRITISH LIBRARY CATALOGUING-IN-PUBLICATION DATA
A catalogue record for this book is available from the
British Library

ISBN 1 85697 183 X

Cover designed by Ian Butterworth
Design and illustration by The Pinpoint Design Company
Printed and bound in Great Britain by BPCC Paulton Books Ltd.

BRILLIANT
THINGS TO
MAKE
AND DO
FOR 6 YEAR OLDS

DEBORAH MANLEY

Kingfisher Books

CONTENTS

HANDY TIPS

Transform a walnut shell into a tiny tortoise,
or make a beautiful necklace out of old tin foil.
With a little imagination, many bits of
household rubbish can be used to make all
kinds of weird and wonderful things.

Start a collecting box...
Keep your eyes open
for possible materials
and store them in a box
or bag.

● old Christmas or
birthday cards and cereal
packets are a good source
of card

● old magazines, postcards and newspapers can be
cut up and used for collages and pictures

● bits of string and wool are always useful

● add old straws, bits of elastic, yoghurt pots, left-
over scraps of material and buttons to your
collecting box

Tools to work with
Here are some of the tools
that you will need:

- a pair of scissors
- a ruler
- a paper punch and a stapler
- sticky tape
- pencils, crayons and felt-tip pens
- a rubber and a pencil sharpener
- paints
- glue – PVA glue is best for making models, but
you can also use glue sticks for sticking paper
and thin card. Whatever kind of glue you are
using, remember to give it plenty of time to dry

Getting ready
Now that you have all the materials ready, you
need somewhere to work.

- always make sure that you
have plenty of room – a clear
table top is ideal, but cover it
with newspaper first

- it is a good idea to cover
yourself with an apron too

Tidying up
When you have finished, don't forget to tidy up.

● put all the lids back on your paints and on the glue pot

● throw away any pieces of paper and card that are too small to save

● put anything you haven't used back into your collecting box

The ideas in this book are just a few of the things that you can make and do. Keep a look-out for other useful materials such as milk bottle tops, old plastic bottles, old corks and matchboxes and try out a few ideas of your own!

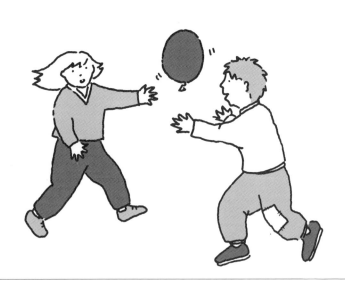

Family picture gallery

Draw or paint a picture of each member of your family and create your own picture gallery.

Dad   Mum

om   Moggie

Bouncer

Swimmer

Polly

Me

Gran   Grandad

HOPSCOTCH

You can draw a hopscotch frame outside on the pavement or on a concrete playground.

You need:
a piece of chalk
a pebble for each
    player

You can play hopscotch on your own or with two or more players competing against each other.

To play, you throw your stone into the numbered squares in turn, starting with square 1. Then you hop along the frame from square to square, leaving out the square with your stone in. On the way back, you bend down, pick up your stone and hop out.

Here are some frames for you to use. With frame A you put both feet down in squares 3 and 4 and squares 6 and 7, so long as your stone is not in them.

If you throw your pebble into the wrong square, or hop on a line, or can't pick up your stone, or fall over, then it is another player's turn. You start your next turn on the square that you ended your last turn in.

KEEP TO THE SQUARES

Some people think that when you walk along the pavement, you should only walk on the squares and not on the lines.

Why do they think this? Well, some people think that if you step on a line, you will turn into a frog. Other people think the bears will get you if you walk on the lines.

So, as you walk along, keep off the lines — make sure your foot always lands safely in a square.

When you're an expert at keeping off the lines, make it a little more difficult for yourself. Try hopping along, keeping off the lines. Try hopping first on one foot and then on the other.

Try taking a hop, then a step and then a jump, still keeping off the lines.

Be sure that you are walking in a safe place well away from the traffic. Cars and lorries are a *real* danger, not a make-believe one!

11

MAKE A MOBILE

When you make a mobile, you must take care to make each piece balance properly.

You need:
cardboard
drinking straws
a paper punch
thread
scissors

1. Draw some squares, triangles and circles on cardboard. Make some big ones and some small ones. You can colour them or draw designs on them if you want. Cut out the shapes.

2. Make a hole in each shape with the paper punch and tie threads of equal length through them.

3. Tie one shape to each end of a straw. Tie another thread round the middle of the straw and slide it along until you find that the shapes on either side hang level.

Now tie the loose end of this thread to one end of another straw. Then tie a shape to the other end of the straw so that the second straw balances.

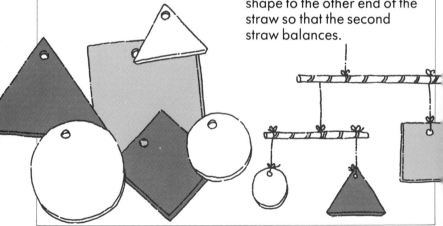

4. Now tie a thread to the middle of this straw. When you hold it up, you should have a small mobile that balances. If one side is heavier than the other, push the threads along until it all hangs straight.

See if you can add more straws and shapes to your mobile.

WHAT'S THAT NOISE?

Take turns with a friend to make sounds and guess what they are. Keep your eyes closed and listen carefully while your friend makes the sounds.

Here are some sounds you can make:

See how many sounds you can guess in a row. When you give up, let your friend become the guesser.

tear a sheet of newspaper
crumple up a piece of
    paper
rattle forks and spoons
    together
jingle coins together
tap the table with your
    fingers
tap the table with your nails
knock on a drawer
knock on the window
open a door
shut a door
rattle keys
tap your toes on the floor
clap your hands
rub your hands against each
    other
knock on your head
yawn
turn on a tap
pour water out of a
    bottle

Silent stalker

If only two people play this game, one sits blindfolded on a chair while the other player creeps up silently from the far end of the room.

If the seated player hears anything, she points to the place the sound is coming from and says, "You're there!"

If she's right, the stalker goes back to the start and begins again. If she's wrong, the stalker carries on.

If the stalker reaches the seated player without being heard, he wins. The players can then change round.

To play with a group, the players stand in a circle around the blindfolded player. One of them is chosen to be the stalker and tries to creep up on the blindfolded player. If they are found out, someone else has a go, but if they manage to reach the centre, it is their turn to be blindfolded.

BE A JEWELLERY MAKER

With some macaroni, some aluminium foil and a paint box you can make yourself some fine pretend jewellery to wear.

Macaroni jewellery

You need:
a packet of short cut
    macaroni
paint and a brush
string

1. Paint the pieces of macaroni in different colours. Leave some in their own colour.

2. Thread them onto string to make necklaces, bracelets and anklets.

NOTE

If you have some wooden or other big beads, these could be strung in with the macaroni.

A silver chain

You need:
aluminium foil
scissors
a stapler

1. Cut strips of foil about
5 cm long by 1 to 2 cm wide.
Make the first link by stapling
the ends of a strip together.

2. Pass the next link through
the first and staple it in the
same way. Continue like this
until your silver chain is long
enough. (You can put a twist
in some of the links so that
they catch the light at
different angles.)

Brooches

You need:
a circle of card about
    5 cm or more across
paint and a brush
a safety pin
sticky tape

1. Paint the card in
brilliant colours to
look like gold and
precious jewels. You can
stick on some sparkle if
you have any.

2. When the paint is quite
dry, put the brooch face
down. Stick a safety pin to
the back with sticky tape.

> **NOTE**
>
> *Brooches can be made in all
> sorts of different shapes and
> styles.*

17

SHADOWS ON THE WALL

Shine a light against a wall. Now stand between the light and the wall to make shadow pictures with your hands.

Here's a turkey.

And here's a goose.

You only need one hand for a sheep.

This is a duck.

But you use two
hands to make a
donkey.

Move your hands
and the bird
will fly.

Is it a dog or is it a
rabbit?

This one is certainly a
dog.

How many more shadow
animals can you make?

19

GAMES FOR JOURNEYS

Here are some games to help pass the time on a long journey.

Sausages
One player is chosen to be IT and has to answer all the questions. But, whatever the others ask, IT must answer "sausages" – and he *must not laugh*, otherwise he is OUT!

What do you wear on your feet?

Sausages.

What's that on your head?

Sausages.

For example:

Who's your favourite popstar?

Sausages.

Think up questions that make the answer as silly as possible to make the player laugh.

Ha ha ha ha ha ha
This is another game to make you laugh, but you must keep a straight face while you're playing it. Players take turns to pass on the laugh. The first player says "ha", the next "ha ha", and so on.

Name two

In this game players take turns to ask the others to give them the names of two of something. One player might say:

Name two animals.

The other replies:

Cat, dog.

You could ask for two people, two places, two flowers, and so on.

Colour bingo

Prepare cards with coloured squares as shown. Write the name of each colour in the squares.

Name

YELLOW	BLUE	RED
GREEN	ORANGE	PURPLE
BROWN	BLACK	WHITE

...PLE

| | BLACK | WHITE |

1. The players watch out for cars or other chosen objects in those colours and put a cross in the right square when they spot one.

2. A player who gets three crosses in a row wins a point.

3. The player who fills in a whole card scores three points. The player with the most points after several games is the winner.

21

HEADS, BODIES AND LEGS

What could a cat-swan-man be? Find out when you play this game for two or more players.

You need:
paper
pencils

1. Each person has a sheet of paper and draws at the top of it the head and neck of an animal.

Try not to let the other players see what you are drawing.

2. Fold the paper over so that only the neck shows and pass it on to the next player.

NOTE

You can have fun making up names for the animals. You can also divide the feet from the legs to make an extra stage in the game.

---

3. Without looking at the heads, everyone draws the body and top of the legs of an animal onto the neck on the piece of paper they now have. Do not look at what has already been drawn on the paper.

4. Fold the paper again, so that only the top of the legs show, and pass it on to the next player.

5. Everyone now draws the legs and feet.

6. Pass on the papers once more and take turns opening up the pictures. See what strange and curious creatures have been invented!

Make a tortoise

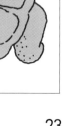

Make a tiny tortoise to
carry in your pocket.

You need:
a walnut
thin card
a pencil
scissors
glue
paint or crayons

1. Open a walnut very
carefully so that the shell
does not break. Lay half the
shell edge down on the card.

2. Draw around the shell,
then add four legs, a head
and a tail.

4. Glue this cut-out firmly to
the edge of the shell.

5. When the glue is dry,
bend the tortoise's legs
downwards so that it can
stand on the ground. Bend its
head upwards a bit so it can
look around.

6. Now your tortoise is
finished. Why not put a
thread around its neck so
that you can pull it along?

3. Paint or colour this shape
to match the shell and
carefully cut it out.

A PICTURE MADE OF SEEDS

Collect seeds, such as rice and barley, dried peas or beans, lentils, orange and apple pips, or melon seeds (dry these in the oven so they go stripy brown).

You can keep your seeds in an egg carton. Put a different kind of seed in each section.

You also need:
a piece of dark coloured card
a pencil
glue
a teaspoon

NOTE

If you want to preserve a seed picture, paint it over very thinly with clear varnish. Try not to let the varnish run off the seedy bits onto the surrounding card.

---

1. Draw a picture on the card. One like this house and garden would work well.

2. Put glue on one small part of the picture. "Paint" that patch by pouring a few seeds from a teaspoon onto the glue. Glue another patch and paint it with other seeds.

3. When you have finished painting the whole picture with seeds, leave it to dry.

GROWING A BEAN

You need:
some broad beans
a saucer
a flowerpot filled with
    earth
water

1. Each bean has a little hole in its covering through which it can take in water. Put your beans in a saucer of water and leave them for about three days.

2. The beans will take in the water and begin to swell.

3. Now plant your beans in a flowerpot or a box of earth. Water the pot. Make sure the earth doesn't dry out while the beans are growing.

4. After about a week, dig up one bean. What has happened to it? Has it put down a root yet? Plant it again.

5. Dig up one of your beans every few days to see how the root is growing. Watch for the shoot to begin to grow upwards.

Once the beans are growing through the earth, put a ruler in the flowerpot. Measure how quickly your beans grow each day.

NOTE

The bean seedlings can be planted out in the garden when they are 8 to 10 cm high.

WHO IS THE FASTEST?

A running race is not the only kind of race you can try. Here are three others.

Hopping

Hop all the way on one foot. If you put the other foot on the ground, you have to go back to the beginning and start again.

Frog race

Squat down with your hands on the ground and hop like a frog.

Wheel race

Stand sideways to the way you will be going. With one step, swing your right foot across in front of you to face the opposite way. With the next stride, swing your left foot across behind you to face the way you began, and so on along the race track.

RACING BALLOONS

Play these two games for six players or more.

Down the row
Divide into two teams and sit in two rows facing each other with your legs stretched out in front of you as shown. Hold one hand behind your back.

Somebody tosses a balloon in between the rows. The players have to try and pat the balloon behind the backs of the other team. If they do, they score a point.

Team throwing
Divide into two teams and form lines down the room. Each team has a balloon. The aim of the game is to be the first team to throw the balloon from one player to another down the line and back again. The balloon must be thrown and the players are not allowed to stand close enough to pass the balloon to each other.

Make an animal mask

You need:
thin card
a pencil
scissors
paint and a brush
elastic or string

3. Make two tiny holes at each side of the mask. Fasten thin elastic or string through the holes. The mask is now ready to wear.

1. Draw the outline of the mask on the card. Add the fur outline and the eye holes.

2. Cut out the mask and the eye holes. Now paint your mask in pussy-cat stripes.

NOTE

With a few changes you can make masks like this for a lion and a tiger, a dog and a wolf. Add long ears and – hey presto! – a rabbit.

Peppermint mice

Make a family of white mice with fondant icing.

You need:

225 gram packet of
    fondant icing
half a teaspoon of
    peppermint essence
some icing sugar
a bowl
a plate
liquorice bootlaces
some chocolate buttons

1. Unwrap the fondant icing, put it in the bowl and knead it gently with your fingers to soften it.

2. Add the peppermint essence a drop at a time, kneading it into the icing until you get the right taste.

3. Mould the icing into sugar mice. Pinch a little of the icing up to form mouse ears.

4. Dust the mice with a little icing sugar.

5. Cut liquorice tails and push one into the back of each mouse. Now add two chocolate drops for eyes.

6. Put your mice on a plate to harden overnight – and hope that they don't run away before morning!

NOTE

If you have some food dye, you could make different coloured mice. You could also roll out the fondant icing and cut out circles and other shapes.

OBSTACLE COURSE

Challenge your friends to an obstacle race! Here are a few ideas for obstacles. You can think up lots more of your own.

Balance a ball on a teaspoon and run with it.

Sit down and eat a dry biscuit with a spoon and fork.

Crawl under a blanket laid out on the ground.

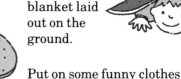

Climb through the legs of a chair.

Put on some funny clothes and wear them to race to the finishing line.

Struggle through a cardboard carton.

Walk down a path blindfolded. Start again if you go off course.

GIANT STEPS

This is a game for at least four players.

Choose one player to be the caller. Everyone else stands in a line some distance away. The caller shows the players the different steps they may use in the game:

Giant steps:
the very longest strides that you can make

Pin steps:
the very shortest steps that you can make on tiptoe

Kangaroo steps:
leaping with feet together

Hopping steps:
hopping along on one foot

Frog steps:
squatting down and hopping along

Then the caller calls out someone's name and tells them what kind of step they can take. For example, "Paul, take two giant steps." Paul must answer, "May I?", and then he can take two giant steps forwards.

The caller gives everyone a chance to move forwards, but if any of the players forget to say "May I?", they must go back to the start.

The player who reaches the leader first is the winner.

Chasing shadows

On sunny days, play with your own shadow and other people's.

Shadow tag
One player is IT and has to "tag" the others by stepping on their shadows.

Shadow changing
Make your shadow change shape as you bend and stretch and move about.

Leave your shadow
Usually your shadow starts right by your feet. But what happens if you jump very high? Can you escape from your shadow?

Short and long

When the sun is high in the sky, your shadow is short. As the sun sinks, your shadow gets longer!

Watch a shadow

Your shadow is always changing because you run around. Choose something that stays still, like a plant or a tree, or a toy. Watch its shadow shrink and grow through the day.

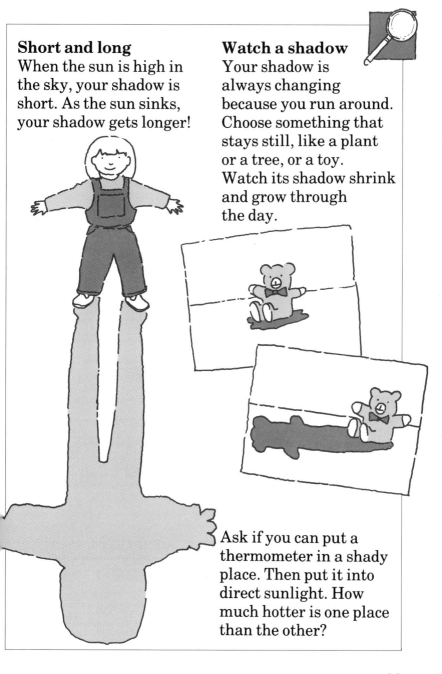

Ask if you can put a thermometer in a shady place. Then put it into direct sunlight. How much hotter is one place than the other?

33

MAKE A BARK RUBBING

Each kind of tree has a different pattern on its bark. Make rubbings from the bark of trees and compare the different patterns.

You need:
paper
a dark crayon

1. Hold the paper over the bark of the tree. Rub the crayon gently over the paper. Soon you will see the bark pattern beginning to show through.

2. Take rubbings from other trees. Compare your bark rubbings. How are they different from one another?

NOTE

You can also make rubbings of coins, using paper and a crayon.

PICTURES FROM LEAVES

Make a collection of leaves. When you have collected a good selection, use them to make a leaf picture.

You need:
thickly mixed paint
white paper
newspaper
a paint brush
leaves

1. Look at a leaf. On one side it is smooth; on the other side you can feel the pattern made by the veins in the leaf. Paint this side of the leaf.

2. Then, very carefully, place the leaf, paint side down, on the white paper. Put some newspaper over it.

3. Rub very gently with your fingers over the newspaper.

4. Lift the newspaper off carefully. Lift off your leaf and what do you find?

5. You can make all kinds of patterns with different leaves.

NOTE

Find out the names of the trees from which the leaves come and write them down beside a picture of each leaf. Learn to recognize the leaves from different trees.

FIND YOUR NAME

This is a good game to get a party started.

1. Write the names of your guests on a piece of card in big letters.

2. Cut up each name into its separate letters.

3. Hide the letters around the room.

As your guests arrive, they have to look for the letters that make up their name. When they have found them, pin them onto the back of their clothes so everyone knows who's who.

NOTE

To make this game more difficult you can add surnames so that everyone has two words to sort out. Try writing the first name in one colour and the surname in another.

RED AND BLACK

This is a good card game for two players.

1. One player has the whole pack, face down. She holds up each card, one at a time, with its back to the other player. He has to guess if it's a red or a black card. If he's right, he keeps the card; if he's wrong, the first player keeps it for her own hand. In this way the two players divide the pack between them. Then the next part of the game begins.

2. The player who made the guesses puts a card face up on the table. The other player puts a second card face up beside it.

3. Then, in turn, the players put one card face up on top of the second card. They do this until a card with the same number as the first card is put on the second pile. Whoever put the card down can take all the cards on the table. Then they put down a new card to start a new round.

The person who collects all the cards is the winner.

FINGER THROWING

This is a guessing game for two players. You can play it anywhere – at home or on a journey.

1. Two players face each other, each with one hand curled into a fist in front of them.

3. On "three", both players uncurl their fists to show some or all of their fingers – or they can keep a tight fist so no fingers show. As they put out their hands, they guess how many fingers the other player will show.

2. One player counts:

ONE TWO THREE!

NOTE

Use a pencil and paper to record the number of correct guesses.

---

4. The winner is the one who is first to guess correctly five times.

Make a telephone

Talk to a friend on your very own telephone.

You need:
two clean yoghurt pots
a length of string (at
    least 3 to 4 metres long)

1. Make a hole in the bottom of each pot. Tie a knot in one end of the string.

2. Thread the string through one pot until the knot holds it. Then thread the other end through the other pot and tie another knot.

3. Make sure the knots are big enough to stop the string pulling through the holes.

4. Each of you takes a pot and moves far enough apart to pull the string taut.

5. Take turns to speak and listen through your pot.

Make a red meal

Plan a meal which will have as many red or reddish-brown coloured things to eat as you can think of. You might choose a tomato salad, red jam tarts and strawberry ice-cream.

You could use a lettuce with red-tinged leaves for a salad, mixed with tomatoes and radishes. Or how about a pinky coloured meat, such as ham or salami, served with tomato chutney?

Make a big jug of blackcurrant juice for a red drink.

Here is a recipe for tomato salad.

You need:
one sliced tomato for
    each person
a teaspoon of brown
    sugar for each tomato
salt and pepper
a dish

1. Lay the tomato slices in a dish. Sprinkle the brown sugar, salt and pepper over them. Leave the salad for at least an hour.

Think about what you would serve if you gave a green meal, or a yellow one. You could even try a red, white and blue one!

COLOURFUL JAM TARTS

These jam tarts are made with different coloured jams.

You need:
200 grams plain flour
100 grams hard
    margarine
some cold water
raspberry or strawberry
    jam (red)
apricot jam or
    marmalade (orange)
lemon curd (yellow)
a bowl
a tablespoon
a pastry cutter
a patty tin

NOTE

The oven should be set at 190°C or gas mark 5. The jam will be very hot when the tarts come out of the oven, so take care!

To make pastry cases:

1. Put the flour in a bowl. Cut up the margarine into little pieces. Rub them into the flour with the tips of your fingers until the mixture looks like breadcrumbs. You may need some help with this.

2. Add the water, a tablespoon at a time, until the mixture forms a ball.

3. Roll out the pastry on a floured surface. Cut out circles with a cutter. Put the circles in a patty tin. Put spoonfuls of the different coloured jams into the pastry circles.

4. Bake your tarts in the oven for 10–15 minutes.

POT OF GOLD

Try this guessing game for two or more players.

One player thinks of an object. He says "If I found a pot of gold, I would buy . . ." and then describes a feature of the object.

The other players have to try and guess what the object is by asking more questions.

For example:
"If I found a pot of gold, I would buy something with two ears."

"What colour?"

"Black and white?"

"How many legs?"

"Four."

"A panda?"

"No."

"Bigger than a panda?"

"Yes."

"A horse?"

"Yes."

THE LADYBIRD GAME

In this game, each player tries to be the first to draw a ladybird.

You will need:
a dice
pencils
paper

Each number on the dice corresponds to a bit of the ladybird's body.

Only when you throw the right number, can you draw that part of your ladybird. You will have to throw lots of fours to get all the legs.

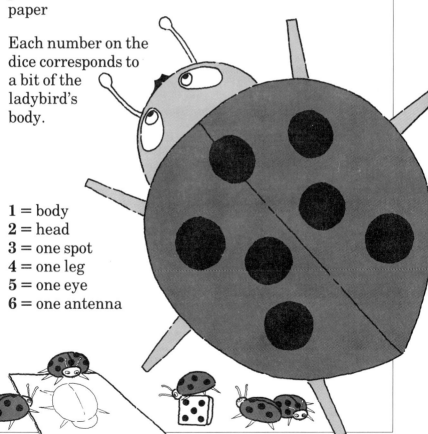

1 = body
2 = head
3 = one spot
4 = one leg
5 = one eye
6 = one antenna

43

MAKE YOURSELF ON PAPER

You need:
a very large sheet of
    paper
a felt-tip pen
scissors
sticky tape
a friend to help you

1. Fasten pieces of paper together with tape to make one really wide piece of paper (wallpaper lining is good).

2. Spread out the sheet of paper on a wide, flat, hard surface like the kitchen floor. You may need to put weights at the corners to stop it rolling up.

3. Lie down in the middle of the paper. Get comfortable so you won't need to move.

4. Now your friend can take the felt-tip pen and draw right round you in one joined-up line. When the drawing is finished, get up and have a look at yourself.

5. Cut out your paper shape and pin it up in your room.

6. Draw round your hands to make outlines of them, too. Draw round your feet as well. Cut out these shapes and stick them onto the paper figure of your body.

Make a glove puppet

You need:
a piece of cloth (about
    20 cm x 12 cm)
a felt-tip pen
a needle and
    thread
two buttons for eyes
wool for hair

1. Cut out two
pieces of cloth
like this, at the
right size
for your
hand. Sew
them together
where the stitch
marks are shown.

2. Turn the
glove shape
inside out.
Sew on the
button eyes.
Add a nose and mouth with a
felt-tip pen or wool stitches.
Sew some loops of wool
hair around the head.

3. If your puppet is an
animal, it will need ears. Cut
these out from scraps of
cloth. Sew them in as shown
above when you sew the two
pieces of cloth together.

4. Put your hand inside your
puppet. Your three middle
fingers go in the wide body
part and your thumb and
little finger go into the
puppet's hands. Talk to your
puppet – before you know
where you are it will be
talking back to you!

MORE
GAMES FOR JOURNEYS

Animal bingo

You need:
bingo cards
a pencil

Prepare a card for each player before you travel. The cards can have the names or pictures of animals on them.

1. The players watch for the animals on their card. When they see one, they point it out and tick if off on their card.

2. Each player who gets a row of three animals across, down or from corner to corner scores a point. The first player to complete their card scores three points. The person with the most points after several games wins.

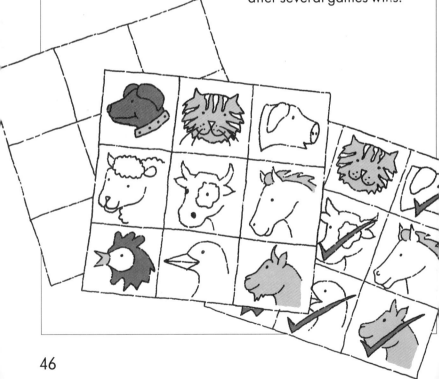

Silly shopping

Take turns to add something silly to the shopping trolley.

1. The first player could say, "I went shopping and I bought a tiger and a bunch of bananas."

2. The second player might continue, "I went shopping and I bought a tiger, a bunch of bananas and a car."

3. The game continues as long as you like. You can have a rule that a player who misses anything from the shopping list drops out. Or try buying things that all start with the same letter.

47

MAKE YOUR OWN JIGSAW

All you need to make your own jigsaw puzzle are two colourful postcards or cards, scissors and an envelope.

1. Cut the cards into 10 or 12 pieces. You can use straight lines or wiggly lines, as you wish. Don't make any of the pieces too small.

2. Mix the pieces of card together in the envelope.

3. Now see how quickly you can sort out the two pictures and put them together again.

48

Ducks fly

This is a very funny game for four or more players. One person is chosen as leader.

The leader stands in front of the others and says, "Ducks fly", while she flaps her arms.

Quickly the others all flap their arms too.

The leader calls out more activities at a good fast pace:

"Pigs grunt" – and she and everyone grunts.

"Horses gallop" – and everyone gallops.

But every now and then the leader tries to catch the others out by saying something wrong, such as, "Mice growl", and growling. Any player who growls is OUT.

ANIMAL GAMES

These are good party games because you need at least five friends to play.

One player is blindfolded and stands in the middle of the room.

Another player taps her on the back. "Who is it," asks the blindfolded player. "Ollie the Octopus," is the reply.

The blindfolded player has to guess who Ollie is. If she's wrong, someone else taps her on the shoulder and she has to guess again. If she's right, Ollie becomes the guesser.

Quack! Moo!
Hide some small prizes, such as sweets, around the room. The players divide into teams – ducks and cows – and choose two leaders.

The team members search for the hidden objects. When someone finds one, he or she has to make the correct animal noise to call their team leader over to collect it. The team that collects the most prizes wins.

Pig

You need:
a pack of playing cards
pencils and paper

The aim is to be the first
person to draw a pig.
Each player is dealt five
cards, face up. If he gets
an Ace, King, Queen or
Jack, he can draw part of
his pig for each of those
cards, in this order: body,
head, four legs (one at a
time) and a curly tail.

If all the cards in the
pack have been dealt and
no one's pig is complete,
shuffle the pack and
carry on playing.

Fish tails

You need:
some newspaper
string

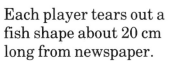

Each player tears out a
fish shape about 20 cm
long from newspaper.
   Tie one end of a piece
of string onto the fish
and the other around
each player's waist. The
fish should lie flat on the
ground. The players face
each other and at "Go!"
they try to "tag" each
other by stepping
on another
player's fish.

Make fresh fruit kebabs

Make these delicious fruit salads on sticks with a choice of fruit pieces. You may need some help getting the fruit ready.

You need:
long cocktail sticks or
    satay sticks
a banana, sliced
some grapes
segments of an orange
some berries
    (strawberries etc.)

NOTE

You can also use chunks of pineapple, and pieces of peaches or apricots.

You can make vegetable kebabs with tiny tomatoes, radishes, slices of cucumber, carrot and courgette, and short pieces of spring onion.

1. String the pieces of fruit onto the sticks. Put different kinds of fruit next to each other so that you get a good mixture of shapes and colours.

2. Serve your fruit kebabs with cream or ice-cream.

A SAUCER GARDEN

Here's a way to grow plants without planting any seeds at all. You grow the plants from the tops cut off root vegetables such as carrots, beetroot and turnips.

You need:
the tops of carrots, turnips and beetroot
a deep saucer or flan dish
some pebbles or gravel
water

1. Scatter the pebbles or gravel in the bottom of the dish. Lay the vegetable tops out on top. Pour water into the dish.

2. Make sure that there is always water in the dish. Now watch your saucer garden of vegetable leaves grow.

FIND THE PAIRS

This card game for two to four players will test your powers of memory!

The aim of the game is to collect pairs of cards with the same number or picture. For example, two tens, two Kings, and so on.

1. Lay a pack of cards out face down on the table or floor.

2. Take turns with the other players to pick up two cards. If the cards have the same number or picture, you can keep them and take another turn. If they are not a pair, you put the cards back *exactly where you found them.* Then it is the next player's turn.

3. Whoever collects the most pairs at the end of the game is the winner.

Beggar my neighbour

This is a fun card game for two people to play.

1. Divide a pack of cards between the two players. Each player's cards are put face down in a pile in front of them.

2. Players take it in turns to place one card face up onto a central pile.

3. If one player turns over an Ace, King, Queen or Jack, the other player has to pay for them like this:
Jack = one card
Queen = two cards
King = three cards
Ace = four cards

4. The player who is paying turns over this number of cards onto the central pile, one by one. If no royal cards or aces come up, the other player takes the whole central pile and puts it at the bottom of his own pile. But if another royal card or ace comes up during payment, he must now pay instead.

5. Sometimes the central pile of cards gets really big before either player wins it. The player who ends up with all the cards wins.

NOTE

This game can go on for a good long time – or it can be over very quickly!

Birthday cards to make and give

Cut out cards

You need:
stiff card about
    20 cm x 15 cm
a pencil
scissors
crayons or coloured
    pencils

1. Fold the card firmly down the centre. Use it with the fold at the top.

2. Draw a picture on the card, making sure that the drawing goes right up to the fold. Colour your drawing. Cut round the drawing and your card will stand up.

Lambs and clouds

This is a good card for someone with a springtime birthday.

You need:
stiff card about
    20 cm x 15 cm
crayons or coloured
    pencils
cotton wool
glue

1. Fold the card in half. Draw a picture of lambs in a field with clouds floating in the sky. Colour your picture.

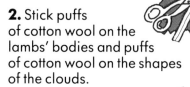

2. Stick puffs of cotton wool on the lambs' bodies and puffs of cotton wool on the shapes of the clouds.

3. Write your birthday greeting inside the card.

NOTE

If you paint the cotton wool other colours, you can use it to make yellow ducklings and brown, fluffy rabbits.

Make a
zigzag number book

A zigzag number book will stand on the shelf so that you can see all the numbers at once.

You need:
a long strip of firm
    paper or thin card
crayons or felt-tip
    pens

4. Stand your number book up on the shelf so that you can look at all the numbers.

1. Fold the strip of paper back and forth like a fan or a concertina so that you have ten spaces.

2. Draw the numbers 1 to 10 on the spaces on one side of the zigzag.

3. Draw a picture for each number to show how many things that number means.

Make a pirate hat

Dress up as a pirate in this black pirate hat.

You need:
thick black paper about
    44 cm x 17 cm
a pencil
scissors
glue, tape or a stapler
white paint
a paint brush

1. Fold the black paper in half. Draw and cut out the two pirate hat shapes.

2. Fasten the two hat pieces together firmly at the sides. Use glue, tape or staples.

3. With the white paint, make a skull and cross-bones on the front of the hat. This is the pirate sign.

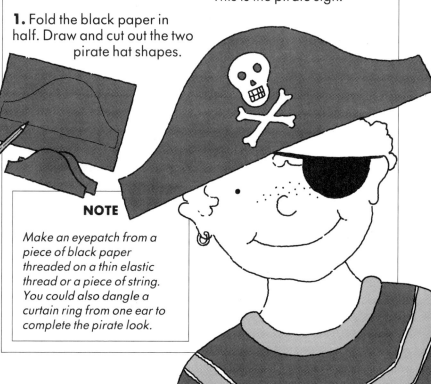

NOTE

Make an eyepatch from a piece of black paper threaded on a thin elastic thread or a piece of string. You could also dangle a curtain ring from one ear to complete the pirate look.

MUSICAL GAMES

Turn on some music and play these games with your friends.

Statues

Everyone dances while the music plays. When the music stops, everyone stands as still as a statue. Anyone who moves is OUT.

Pass the parcel

Wrap a small prize in layers of paper. While the music plays, the players pass the parcel around in a circle. Each time the music stops, the person holding the parcel takes off one layer of paper.

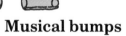

Musical bumps

Everyone dances while the music plays. When the music stops, everyone bumps down onto the floor. The last one down is OUT.

NOTE

Taped music is best for these games as it is easy to stop and start.

Musical islands
Place some pieces of cardboard around the floor of the room. You need one piece fewer than the number of players. While the music plays, everyone dances. As soon as the music stops, they must step onto one of the "islands". Only one person is allowed on an island. The person who is left without an island is OUT.

Take away an island each time the music starts up again.

61

INDEX

Action games

 ## See how it works

 ## Board and table games